THE ULTIMATE
CAROLINA PANTHERS
TRIVIA BOOK

A Collection of Amazing Trivia Quizzes
and Fun Facts for Die-Hard Panthers Fans!

Ray Walker

Exclusive Free Book
Crazy Sports Stories

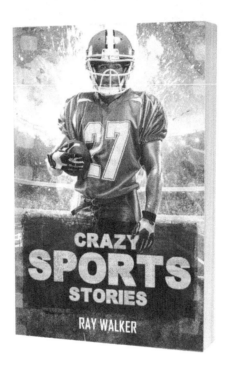

As a thank you for getting a copy of this book I would like to offer you a free copy of my book Crazy Sports Stories which comes packed with interesting stories from your favorite sports such as Football, Hockey, Baseball, Basketball and more.

Grab your free copy over at

RayWalkerMedia.com/Bonus

CONTENTS

INTRODUCTION

The Carolina Panthers were established in 1995 in Clemson, South Carolina. The Panthers have consistently proven themselves to be a team that fights hard and is a force to be reckoned with in the NFL.

Although they have yet to win the championship, they have made it to the Super Bowl twice. They have won two NFC championships, five NFC South division championships, and one NFC West division championship. They are very often a threat in the NFC South, having last won it in 2015. They have made eight NFL playoff appearances, with their most recent Super Bowl appearance being 2015.

The Panthers have retired the number of only one player, Sam Mills. They do have a Hall of Honor, though, which was formed in 1997 to enshrine their best players of the past. Panthers Hall of Honor members are Jake Delhomme, Jordan Gross, Mike McCormack, Sam Mills, Steve Smith, and Wesley Walls.

Football is a lot like life. There are good times and bad times, good days and bad days, but you have to do your absolute best to never give up. The Carolina Panthers have proven that they refuse to give up and that they will do anything they need to do to bring a championship to the Carolinas. Winning is more than possible when you have a storied past, as the Panthers do. They have so much captivating history and so many undeniable player legacies to be profoundly proud of.

The Panthers' current home is Bank of America Stadium, which opened in 1996 in Charlotte, North Carolina. They play in one of the most difficult divisions in the NFL, the NFC South, alongside the New Orleans Saints, Atlanta Falcons, and Tampa Bay Buccaneers.

With such a rich past containing countless moments of triumph and heartbreak, you're probably already very knowledgeable as the die-hard Panthers fan that you are. Let's test that knowledge to see if you truly are the world's biggest Panthers fan.

CHAPTER 1:

ORIGINS & HISTORY

QUIZ TIME!

1. Which of the following team names did the franchise once go by?

    a. Cats

    b. Leopards

    c. Cheetahs

    d. None of the above; they have always been the Panthers.

2. In what year was the Carolina Panthers franchise established?

    a. 1985

    b. 1989

    c. 1995

    d. 1999

3. The Panthers' current home is Bank of America Stadium.

    a. True

    b. False

4. Which division do the Carolina Panthers play in?

   a. NFC South

   b. AFC South

   c. NFC West

   d. AFC West

5. The Carolina Panthers were a member of the NFC West Division from 1995 to 2001.

   a. True

   b. False

6. How many NFC championships has the Panthers franchise won (as of the end of the 2020 season)?

   a. 2

   b. 3

   c. 6

   d. 9

7. What is the name of the Panthers' mascot?

   a. Purr Panther

   b. Sir Purr

   c. Paul Panther

   d. Panther Patrick

8. Who is the winningest head coach in Carolina Panthers history (as of the end of the 2020 season)?

   a. Dom Capers

   b. George Seifert

   c. Ron Rivera

   d. John Fox

9. Where is Bank of America Stadium located?

    a. Myrtle Beach, South Carolina
    b. Charleston, South Carolina
    c. Raleigh, North Carolina
    d. Charlotte, North Carolina

10. Who was the first head coach of the Panthers?

    a. Ron Rivera
    b. Perry Fewell
    c. Dom Capers
    d. John Fox

11. The Carolina Panthers played their home games at Memorial Stadium in Clemson, South Carolina, during their inaugural season.

    a. True
    b. False

12. Who is the current owner of the Carolina Panthers organization?

    a. Arthur Blank
    b. Jim Irsay
    c. Jed York
    d. David Tepper

13. How many appearances have the Carolina Panthers franchise made in the NFL playoffs (as of the end of the 2020 season)?

    a. 5
    b. 8

c. 10

d. 12

14. How many Super Bowl titles have the Panthers won (as of the end of the 2019 season)?

    a. 0

    b. 1

    c. 2

    d. 3

15. The Carolina Panthers never won a division title during their time in the NFC West.

    a. True

    b. False

16. Who was the general manager of the Carolina Panthers organization from 2002 to 2012 and 2017 to 2020?

    a. John Lynch

    b. Kevin Colbert

    c. Marty Hurney

    d. Mike Mayock

17. How many NFC South division titles have the Carolina Panthers won (as of the end of the 2020 season)?

    a. 2

    b. 4

    c. 5

    d. 7

18. Who is the current head coach of the Carolina Panthers?

a. Ron Rivera

b. John Fox

c. Perry Fewell

d. Matt Rhule

19. Teddy Bridgewater is the current quarterback of the Carolina Panthers (as of the 2020 season).

a. True

b. False

20. Jerry Richardson was the original owner and founder of the Carolina Panthers organization.

a. True

b. False

QUIZ ANSWERS

1. D – None of the above; they have always been the Panthers.

2. C – 1995

3. A – True

4. A – NFC South

5. A – True

6. A – 2

7. B – Sir Purr

8. C – Ron Rivera

9. D – Charlotte, North Carolina

10. C – Dom Capers

11. A – True

12. D – David Tepper

13. B – 8

14. A – 0

15. B – False (They won a division title in 1996.)

16. C – Marty Hurney

17. C – 5

18. D – Matt Rhule

19. A – True

20. A – True

DID YOU KNOW?

1. The Carolina Panthers have had six head coaches so far: Dom Capers, George Seifert, John Fox, Ron Rivera, Perry Fewell, and Matt Rhule.

2. The Carolina Panthers' current head coach is Matt Rhule. He was previously the assistant offensive line coach for the New York Giants and the head coach at Temple University and Baylor University, among several other coaching jobs. He was named the Big 12 Coach of the Year in 2019.

3. Ron Rivera is the Carolina Panthers' all-time winningest head coach with a record of 76-63-1. Rivera was fired in the middle of the 2019 season due to new ownership wanting change. He became the head coach of the Washington Football Team in 2020.

4. The Carolina Panthers Hall of Honor was established in 1997 to honor players/coaches/members of the organization for their contributions to the franchise. Members of the Hall of Honor are Jake Delhomme, Jordan Gross, Mike McCormack, Sam Mills, Steve Smith, and Wesley Walls.

5. Neither Charlotte nor the Panthers have ever hosted the Super Bowl. The two Super Bowls that the Panthers have participated in were in Houston, Texas, and Santa Clara, California.

6. The current president of the Carolina Panthers organization is Tom Glick. The 2020 season was his third

season in the role. He oversees the team's day-to-day operations. He was previously the president of the New York City FC and a board member for the Derby County Football Club.

7. The Carolina Panthers have made two Super Bowl appearances so far. In the Super Bowls they have appeared in, they have faced the New England Patriots and the Denver Broncos.

8. The current owner of the Carolina Panthers is David Tepper. Tepper is a billionaire businessman and philanthropist. He also owns Charlotte FC of Major League Soccer (MLS). He is the founder and president of Appaloosa Management, a global hedge fund.

9. The Panthers' mascot, Sir Purr, is a panther himself. His favorite foods include "falcons, eagles, and seahawks." He has a rivalry with Jaxson de Ville, the mascot of the Jacksonville Jaguars.

10. According to *Forbes* magazine, the Carolina Panthers organization is worth approximately $2.3 billion. The Panthers' salary cap for the 2020 season was an estimated $205,244,686.

CHAPTER 2:

JERSEYS & NUMBERS

QUIZ TIME!

1. The shape of the Panthers' logo was designed to resemble the outline of both North Carolina and South Carolina.

   a. True

   b. False

2. What are the Panthers' current team colors?

   a. Panther blue, black, and gray

   b. Navy blue, black, and silver

   c. Panther blue, black, and silver

   d. Baby blue, black, and silver

3. NFL regulations allow the Panthers to use their alternate blue jerseys only twice each NFL season.

   a. True

   b. False

4. Which of the following numbers is the ONLY number retired by the Carolina Panthers?

a. 31

b. 51

c. 61

d. 81

5. What number does quarterback Teddy Bridgewater currently wear?

   a. 2

   b. 3

   c. 4

   d. 5

6. What number did quarterback Cam Newton wear with the Panthers?

   a. 1

   b. 5

   c. 15

   d. 25

7. Current Panthers kicker Joey Slye wears number 4.

   a. True

   b. False

8. What number did Steve Smith wear with the Panthers?

   a. 71

   b. 79

   c. 81

   d. 89

9. What number did Luke Kuechly wear with the Panthers?

    a. 50
    b. 59
    c. 60
    d. 69

10. While he was with the Carolina Panthers, Julius Peppers wore number 90.

    a. True
    b. False

11. What number did Jordan Gross wear with the Panthers?

    a. 30
    b. 39
    c. 60
    d. 69

12. What number did Thomas Davis wear with the Panthers?

    a. 47
    b. 58
    c. 67
    d. Both A and B

13. Kevin Greene's number 91 was retired by the Panthers in 2012.

    a. True
    b. False

14. What number does Tahir Whitehead currently wear for the Panthers?

a. 50

b. 52

c. 59

d. 60

15. What number did Mushin Muhammad wear with the Panthers?

    a. 80

    b. 87

    c. 90

    d. 97

16. What number did Ryan Kalil wear with the Panthers?

    a. 55

    b. 65

    c. 67

    d. Both B and C

17. What number did Mike Minter wear with the Panthers?

    a. 10

    b. 20

    c. 30

    d. 40

18. What number did Mike Rucker wear with the Panthers?

    a. 63

    b. 73

    c. 83

    d. 93

19. What number did quarterback Jake Delhomme wear with the Panthers?

    a. 9
    b. 12
    c. 17
    d. None of the above

20. While with the Carolina Panthers, DeAngelo Williams wore number 43.

    a. True
    b. False

QUIZ ANSWERS

1. A – True

2. C – Panther blue, black, and silver

3. A – True

4. B – 51 (Sam Mills)

5. D – 5

6. A – 1

7. A – True

8. D – 89

9. B – 59

10. A – True

11. D – 69

12. D – Both A and B

13. B – False

14. B – 52

15. B – 87

16. D – Both B and C

17. C – 30

18. D – 93

19. C – 17

20. B – False (He wore number 34.)

DID YOU KNOW?

1. Original Panthers owner and founder Jerry Richardson said that no uniform changes would be made in his lifetime.

2. During the 2019 season, the Panthers wore a 25th anniversary patch on their uniforms.

3. The Panthers' all-black uniforms won the Greatest Uniform in NFL History contest, a fan-voted contest run by NFL.com in July of 2013.

4. In 2012, the collar on the Panthers' jerseys was altered to honor former Panthers player and coach Sam Mills by featuring the phrase "Keep Pounding."

5. While with the Panthers, kicker John Kasay wore number 4.

6. Current Panthers running back Christian McCaffrey wears number 22.

7. While with the Panthers, tight end Greg Olsen wore the number 88.

8. While with the Panthers, Kevin Greene wore the number 91.

9. While with the Panthers, running back Jonathan Stewart wore the number 28.

10. While with the Panthers, Reggie White wore the number 92.

CHAPTER 3:

THE NATIONAL FOOTBALL LEAGUE

QUIZ TIME!

1. How many total teams play in the NFL?

    a. 20

    b. 25

    c. 30

    d. 32

2. The National Football League was founded in 1920.

    a. True

    b. False

3. Who is the current commissioner of the National Football League?

    a. Elmer Layden

    b. Pete Rozelle

    c. Roger Goodell

    d. Paul Tagliabue

4. The NFL is the wealthiest professional sports league.

    a. True
    b. False

5. Where is the NFL headquarters located?

    a. Phoenix, Arizona
    b. New York, New York
    c. Los Angeles, California
    d. Boston, Massachusetts

6. As of the 2021 season, how many games does each NFL team play per season?

    a. 12
    b. 16
    c. 17
    d. 20

7. The San Francisco 49ers have won the most championships in NFL history.

    a. True
    b. False

8. Where is the Pro Football Hall of Fame located?

    a. Seattle, Washington
    b. Los Angeles, California
    c. Cooperstown, New York
    d. Canton, Ohio

9. Which current NFL stadium is the oldest NFL stadium in use?

a. Lambeau Field

b. Soldier Field

c. Arrowhead Stadium

d. New Era Field

10. What year were helmets made mandatory in the NFL?

a. 1940

b. 1943

c. 1947

d. 1950

11. What year was the first NFL game televised?

a. 1935

b. 1937

c. 1939

d. 1940

12. All footballs used in NFL games come from a Wilson factory in Ada, Ohio.

a. True

b. False

13. The Super Bowl trophy is known as the _____ Trophy.

a. Layden

b. Lombardi

c. Halas

d. Hunt

14. What team won the first Super Bowl?

a. Kansas City Chiefs

b. Baltimore Ravens

c. New York Jets

d. Green Bay Packers

15. How many cows does it take to supply the leather needed to make the NFL's footballs per season?

a. 500

b. 1,000

c. 2,000

d. 3,000

16. The Baltimore Colts were the first NFL team to have cheerleaders.

a. True

b. False

17. Which African-American football player broke the NFL color barrier?

a. Joe Lillard

b. Ray Kemp

c. Kenny Washington

d. Marlin Briscoe

18. Which NFL team has the most retired numbers?

a. Green Bay Packers

b. Pittsburgh Steelers

c. San Francisco 49ers

d. Chicago Bears

19. What year did referees begin using penalty flags in the NFL?

    a. 1945
    b. 1948
    c. 1951
    d. 1955

20. Lyndon B. Johnson was the first U.S. President to attend an NFL game while in office.

    a. True
    b. False

QUIZ ANSWERS

1. D – 32

2. A – True

3. C – Roger Goodell

4. A – True

5. B – New York, New York

6. C – 17

7. B – False (The Green Bay Packers have won 13 championships.)

8. D – Canton, Ohio

9. B – Soldier Field

10. B – 1943

11. C – 1939

12. A – True

13. B – Lombardi

14. D – Green Bay Packers

15. D – 3,000

16. A – True

17. C – Kenny Washington

18. D – Chicago Bears (13)

19. B – 1948

20. A – True

DID YOU KNOW?

1. Steve Young is the only left-handed quarterback in the Pro Football Hall of Fame.

2. *Monday Night Football* made its debut on ABC on September 21, 1970.

3. The 1973 Miami Dolphins are the first and only NFL team in history to have a perfect, undefeated season.

4. NFL referees first began wearing wireless microphones during the 1975 season.

5. Instant replay in the NFL was established during the 1986 season.

6. Every active NFL team has won a playoff game at least once.

7. The Arizona Cardinals are older than the state of Arizona. The Cardinals franchise was founded in 1898, while the state of Arizona was granted statehood in 1912.

8. The Philadelphia Eagles are the only team in the NFL with a logo that faces the left.

9. NFL cheerleaders make approximately $70-$90 per game.

10. Only 8.01% of the money made from pink NFL merchandise actually goes towards breast cancer research.

CHAPTER 4:

CATCHY NICKNAMES

QUIZ TIME!

1. What is Cam Newton's nickname?

    a. Batman
    b. The Flash
    c. Superman
    d. The Green Arrow

2. Muhsin Muhammad had the nickname "Moose."

    a. True
    b. False

3. What nickname does Luke Kuechly go by?

    a. The Hulk
    b. Captain America
    c. Iron Man
    d. Thor

4. What nickname does Ron Rivera go by?

    a. Riverboat Ron
    b. Chico

c. Shy Ronnie

d. Both A and B

5. What is Julius Peppers's nickname?

a. Black Pepper

b. Orange Julius

c. The Freak of Nature

d. Hot Sauce

6. What nickname did Sam Mills go by?

a. Super Sam

b. Field Mouse

c. Sam I Am

d. Keep Pounding

7. Reggie White had the nickname "The Minister of Defense."

a. True

b. False

8. "Dino" is a nickname. What is Dino Philyaw's full name?

a. Dwight Drake Philyaw

b. David Philyaw

c. Daniel Philyaw

d. Delvic Dyvon Philyaw

9. "Wesley" is Wesley Walls's middle name. What is his first name?

a. Keith

b. Ned

c. Charles

d. Eugene

10. "Mark" is Mark Carrier's middle name. What is his first name?

    a. John

    b. Zach

    c. Matthew

    d. Miles

11. "J.J." is a nickname. What is J.J. Jansen's full name?

    a. Justin Richard Jansen

    b. Jeffrey Richard Jansen

    c. Jacob Jeremy Jansen

    d. Joshua Joseph Jansen

12. The Panthers cheerleaders are called the Topcats.

    a. True

    b. False

13. "D.J." is a nickname. What is D.J. Moore's full name?

    a. Dustin Jacob Moore Jr.

    b. David Moore Jr.

    c. Daniel James Moore

    d. Denniston Moore Jr.

14. "Fozzy" is a nickname. What is Fozzy Whitaker's full name?

    a. Foswhitt Jer'ald Whittaker

    b. Franklin Gerald Whitaker

    c. Fosworth Beauregard Whitaker

    d. Frederick Whitaker

15. "Toi" is a nickname. Toi Cook's first tame is Timothy.

    a. True
    b. False

16. "Al" is a nickname. What is Al Wallace's full name?

    a. Alvin Dwight Wallace
    b. Salvador James Wallace
    c. Alonzo Dwight Wallace
    d. Calvin James Wallace

17. Star Lotulelei's full first name is Starlite.

    a. True
    b. False

18. "A.J." is a nickname. What is A.J. Klein's full name?

    a. Arthur Joseph Klein
    b. Albert Jacob Klein
    c. Alexander Jerimiah Klein
    d. Aaron James Klein

19. What nickname did Bene Benwikere go by?

    a. Bene Baller
    b. Big B
    c. Big Play Bene
    d. Beneficial

20. "D.J." is a nickname. D.J. Hackett's full name is DeAndre James Hackett.

    a. True
    b. False

QUIZ ANSWERS

1. C – Superman

2. A – True

3. B – Captain America

4. D – Both A and B

5. C – The Freak of Nature

6. B – Field Mouse

7. A – True

8. D – Delvic Dyvon Philyaw

9. C – Charles

10. A – John

11. B – Jeffrey Richard Jansen

12. A – True

13. D – Denniston Moore Jr.

14. A – Foswhitt Jer'ald Whittaker

15. B – False (Toi is his given first name.)

16. C – Alonzo Dwight Wallace

17. A – True

18. D – Aaron James Klein

19. C – Big Play Bene

20. A – True

DID YOU KNOW?

1. Teddy Bridgewater is referred to by some as "Teddy Two Gloves" because he is one of the only current NFL quarterbacks who wears gloves on both hands while playing.

2. Former Panther Corey Brown goes by the nickname "Philly."

3. Current Panther Phillip Walker goes by the nickname "P.J."

4. Current Panther Pharoh Cooper goes by the nickname "The South Carolina Pharoh."

5. Current Panther Eli Apple goes by the nickname "The Quiet Assassin."

6. Former Panther Chris Hogan goes by the nickname "7-Eleven."

7. Former Panther Vernon Butler goes by the nickname "Big Vern."

8. Former Panther Charles Tillman goes by the nickname "Peanut."

9. Former Panther Greg Hardy goes by the nickname "The Kraken."

10. Former Panther Frank Kearse goes by the nickname "Big Spoon."

CHAPTER 5:

THE FREAK OF NATURE

QUIZ TIME!

1. What is Julius Peppers's full name?

    a. Julius Raymond Peppers

    b. Julius Frazier Peppers

    c. Kevin Julius Peppers

    d. Matthew Julius Peppers

2. Julius Pepper played his entire 17-season NFL career with the Carolina Panthers.

    a. True

    b. False

3. Where was Julius Peppers born?

    a. Wilson, North Carolina

    b. San Francisco, California

    c. Charleston, South Carolina

    d. Chicago, Illinois

4. When was Julius Peppers born?

    a. December 18, 1980
    b. December 18, 1985
    c. January 18, 1985
    d. January 18, 1980

5. Julius Peppers began and ended his NFL career with the Carolina Panthers.

    a. True
    b. False

6. How many Pro Bowls was Julius Peppers named to in his 17-season NFL career?

    a. 3
    b. 7
    c. 9
    d. 10

7. Where did Julius Peppers go to college?

    a. Texas A&M University
    b. University of South Carolina
    c. Clemson University
    d. University of North Carolina at Chapel Hill

8. Julius Peppers was drafted by the Carolina Panthers in the 1st round of the 2002 NFL Draft, 2nd overall.

    a. True
    b. False

9. How many times was Julius Peppers named a First Team All-Pro?

a. 1

b. 3

c. 4

d. 6

10. How many Super Bowls did Julius Peppers win?

a. 0

b. 1

c. 2

d. 3

11. Julius Peppers holds the NFL record for most career forced fumbles, with _____.

a. 33

b. 44

c. 55

d. 66

12. Julius Peppers was named the NFL Defensive Rookie of the Year in 2002.

a. True

b. False

13. How many times was Julius Pepper named the NFC Defensive Player of the Week?

a. 4

b. 5

c. 7

d. 9

14. Julius Pepper was named the NFC Defensive Player of the Month four times.

    a. True
    b. False

15. Julius Peppers holds the franchise record for most career sacks, with _____.

    a. 77
    b. 87
    c. 97
    d. 107

16. At the University of North Carolina, Julius Peppers was also on the _____ team.

    a. Baseball
    b. Basketball
    c. Soccer
    d. Hockey

17. Julius Peppers was named to the HOF 2000s and 2010s All-Decade Teams.

    a. True
    b. False

18. On May 8, 2019, Julius Peppers was hired as _____ with the Carolina Panthers.

    a. Director of Football Operations
    b. Director of Player Wellness
    c. Special Assistant of Business Operations
    d. Defensive Assistant Coach

19. With the Carolina Panthers, Julius Peppers wore number
    _____.

    a. 56
    b. 65
    c. 80
    d. 90

20. Julius Peppers was named the NFL Rookie of the Month
    for October 2002.

    a. True
    b. False

QUIZ ANSWERS

1. B – Julius Frazier Peppers
2. B – False (He played with the Panthers, Chicago Bears, and Green Bay Packers.)
3. A – Wilson, North Carolina
4. D – January 18, 1980
5. A – True (2002-2009 and 2017-2018)
6. C – 9
7. D – University of North Carolina at Chapel Hill
8. A – True
9. B – 3
10. A – 0
11. C – 55
12. A – True
13. C – 7
14. A – True
15. C – 97
16. B – Basketball
17. A – True
18. C – Special Assistant of Business Operations
19. D – 90
20. A – True

DID YOU KNOW?

1. Julius Peppers finished his NFL career with 715 tackles and 159.5 sacks. He also had 79 pass deflections, 11 interceptions, 51 forced fumbles, and six defensive touchdowns.

2. Julius Peppers was named a Second Team All-Pro three times.

3. Julius Peppers was named a unanimous All-American in 2001. That same year, he won the Lombardi Award and Chuck Bednarik Award.

4. Julius Peppers played for the Carolina Panthers from 2002 to 2009, the Chicago Bears from 2010 to 2013, the Green Bay Packers from 2014 to 2016, and again with the Panthers from 2017 to 2018. He has been named one of the 100 Greatest Chicago Bears of all time.

5. In 2005, Julius Peppers was named one of the 50 Greatest Athletes from the Twin County area by the *Rocky Mount Telegram*.

6. During his senior year of high school, Julius Peppers was named Male Athlete of the Year by the North Carolina High School Athletic Association. He played football and track while in high school.

7. Julius Peppers made his NFL debut on September 8, 2002, against the Baltimore Ravens.

8. Julius Peppers and Donovan McNabb are the only people ever to play in both the NCAA men's basketball Final Four and the NFL's Super Bowl. Donovan McNabb was a quarterback for the Philadelphia Eagles, Washington Redskins, and Minnesota Vikings.

9. Julius Peppers attended Southern Nash High School in Bailey, North Carolina. He went to college at the University of North Carolina at Chapel Hill. Being born in North Carolina as well, he was a great fit for the Panthers.

10. Julius Peppers wore the number 90 with the Carolina Panthers and Chicago Bears and the number 56 with the Green Bay Packers.

CHAPTER 6:

STATISTICALLY SPEAKING

QUIZ TIME!

1. Who holds the Carolina Panthers franchise record for the most points scored in a single season with 146 in 2015?

   a. John Kasay
   b. DeAngelo Williams
   c. Graham Gano
   d. Steve Smith

2. John Kasay holds the Carolina Panthers franchise record for the most career points, with 1,482.

   a. True
   b. False

3. Which of the following head coaches holds the franchise record for the most playoff appearances with the Panthers?

   a. Dom Capers
   b. John Fox
   c. George Seifert
   d. Ron Rivera

4. Cam Newton holds the Carolina Panthers franchise record for the most passing yards in a single game, with _____ yards.

   a. 422
   b. 432
   c. 442
   d. 452

5. Which player holds the Carolina Panthers franchise record for most sacks in a single season with 15 in 1998?

   a. Lamar Lathon
   b. Julius Peppers
   c. Greg Hardy
   d. Kevin Greene

6. Which player holds the Carolina Panthers franchise record for most career sacks, with 97?

   a. Charles Johnson
   b. Julius Peppers
   c. Mike Rucker
   d. Kevin Greene

7. Doug Evans holds the franchise record for interceptions in a single season with eight in 2001.

   a. True
   b. False

8. Who holds the Carolina Panthers franchise record for most career interceptions, with 27?

   a. Luke Kuechly
   b. Mike Minter

c. Chris Gamble

d. Eric Davis

9. Steve Smith holds the Carolina Panthers franchise record for the most receiving yards in a single game, with _____ yards.

    a. 208

    b. 218

    c. 228

    d. 248

10. DeAngelo Williams holds the Carolina Panthers franchise record for the most rushing yards in a single game, with _____ yards.

    a. 210

    b. 220

    c. 230

    d. 250

11. Who holds the Carolina Panthers franchise record for most career rushing attempts, with 1,669 attempts?

    a. Cam Newton

    b. DeShaun Foster

    c. DeAngelo Williams

    d. Jonathan Stewart

12. Steve Smith holds the Carolina Panthers franchise records for most career receptions (836) and most receptions in a single season (103 in 2005).

    a. True

    b. False

13. DeAngelo Williams holds the Carolina Panthers franchise record for most rushing yards in a single season with 1,515 in _____.

    a. 2006
    b. 2008
    c. 2012
    d. 2014

14. Who holds the Carolina Panthers franchise record for most passing completions in a single season with 343 in 1999?

    a. Rodney Peete
    b. Jake Delhomme
    c. Cam Newton
    d. Steve Beuerlein

15. Cam Newton holds the Carolina Panthers franchise record for most career passing completions, with _____.

    a. 2,171
    b. 2,271
    c. 2,371
    d. 2,471

16. As of the end of the 2019 season, the franchise's longest winning streak within one season is ____ games (2015).

    a. 10
    b. 12
    c. 14
    d. 16

17. The Carolina Panthers' largest win margin came on December 13, 2015, against the Atlanta Falcons, whom they beat by a score of 38-0.

    a. True
    b. False

18. As of the end of the 2020 season, the Carolina Panthers franchise recorded the most wins in a single regular season with _____ in 2015.

    a. 13
    b. 14
    c. 15
    d. 16

19. Who holds the Carolina Panthers franchise record for most playoff games as head coach, with eight?

    a. Ron Rivera
    b. John Fox
    c. Matt Rhule
    d. Dom Capers

20. The Carolina Panthers' largest loss margin came on December 24, 2000, against the Oakland Raiders, whom they lost to by a score of 9-52.

    a. True
    b. False

QUIZ ANSWERS

1. C – Graham Gano

2. A – True

3. D – Ron Rivera (4)

4. B – 432

5. D – Kevin Greene

6. B – Julius Peppers

7. A – True

8. C – Chris Gamble

9. B – 218

10. A – 210

11. D – Jonathan Stewart

12. A – True

13. B – 2008

14. D – Steve Beuerlein

15. C – 2,371

16. C – 14

17. A – True

18. C – 15

19. B – John Fox

20. A – True

DID YOU KNOW?

1. The Carolina Panthers franchise record for highest attendance in a single season was in 2015 when 592,454 total fans attended games at Bank of America Stadium.

2. The franchise record for highest attendance at Memorial Stadium was set on December 10, 1995 when 76,136 fans were in attendance. The franchise record for highest attendance at Bank of America Stadium took place on November 8, 2015, when 74,461 fans were in attendance.

3. The Panthers franchise record for highest attendance at a road game occurred on September 28, 2009, at AT&T Stadium vs the Dallas Cowboys when a whopping 90,588 fans were in attendance.

4. John Kasay holds the Carolina Panthers franchise record for most field goals made in a single season with 37 in 1996. He also holds the franchise record for most career field goals made, with 351.

5. DeAngelo Williams holds the franchise record for most touchdowns in a season with 18 in 2008.

6. John Fox holds the Carolina Panthers franchise record for most regular-season games as head coach, with 144 games.

7. The Carolina Panthers' first playoff game was a 26-17 win over the Dallas Cowboys on January 5, 1997.

8. The Carolina Panthers' first regular-season game was a 23-20 OT loss to the Atlanta Falcons on September 3, 1995.

9. The Carolina Panthers franchise record for fewest wins in a single season was one in 2001.

10. The Carolina Panthers franchise record for most points scored in a season was 500 in 2015.

CHAPTER 7:

THE TRADE MARKET

QUIZ TIME!

1. On May 30, 1995, the Carolina Panthers traded a 1996 6th round draft pick to the _____ for Barry Foster.

    a. Dallas Cowboys

    b. San Francisco 49ers

    c. Pittsburgh Steelers

    d. Miami Dolphins

2. On August 25, 1996, the Carolina Panthers traded a 1997 5th round draft pick to the _____ in exchange for Raghib Ismail.

    a. Kansas City Chiefs

    b. New York Jets

    c. Seattle Seahawks

    d. Oakland Raiders

3. The Carolina Panthers did not make a trade in 1997.

    a. True

    b. False

4. On July 23, 1998, the Carolina Panthers traded _____ to the Indianapolis Colts in exchange for a 1999 2nd round pick (Chris Terry).

    a. Michael Bates
    b. Tyrone Poole
    c. Sam Mills
    d. Mike Minter

5. On April 21, 2000, the Carolina Panthers traded Fred Lane to the Indianapolis Colts for Spencer Reid.

    a. True
    b. False

6. On September 2, 2001, the Carolina Panthers traded a 2002 7th round draft pick to the _____ for Perry Phenix.

    a. New England Patriots
    b. Baltimore Ravens
    c. Pittsburgh Pirates
    d. Tennessee Titans

7. On July 19, 2002, the Carolina Panthers traded Jay Williams to the _____ for Al Wallace and a 2003 4th round draft pick (Colin Branch).

    a. Philadelphia Eagles
    b. St. Louis Rams
    c. Miami Dolphins
    d. Detroit Lions

8. On September 4, 2004, the Carolina Panthers traded an undisclosed 2004 draft pick to the Pittsburgh Steelers for _____.

a. Rodney Peete
b. Todd Fordham
c. Chris Gamble
d. Mike Rucker

9. On May 19, 2005, the Carolina Panthers traded Todd Sauerbrun to the _____ for Jason Baker and an undisclosed 2005 draft pick.

a. Washington Redskins
b. Green Bay Packers
c. Cincinnati Bengals
d. Denver Broncos

10. The Carolina Panthers did not make a trade in 2006.

a. True
b. False

11. On August 2, 2007, the Carolina Panthers traded an undisclosed 2007 draft pick to the _____ for Chris Harris.

a. New York Jets
b. Chicago Bears
c. Seattle Seahawks
d. San Diego Chargers

12. On August 30, 2008, the Carolina Panthers traded an undisclosed 2008 draft pick to the Miami Dolphins for Josh McCown.

a. True
b. False

13. On April 13, 2009, the Carolina Panthers traded an undisclosed 2009 draft pick to the Green Bay Packers for

_____.

    a. Jake Delhomme

    b. Muhsin Muhammad

    c. J.J. Jansen

    d. Julius Peppers

14. On September 1, 2009, the Carolina Panthers traded a 2009 3rd round draft pick to the Cleveland Browns for Louis Leonard.

    a. True

    b. False

15. On April 27, 2010, the Carolina Panthers traded Chris Harris to the _____ for Jamar Williams.

    a. Chicago Bears

    b. Detroit Lions

    c. Jacksonville Jaguars

    d. New England Patriots

16. On July 29, 2011, the Carolina Panthers traded a 2012 3rd round draft pick (Brandon Taylor) to the Chicago Bears for

_____.

    a. Brandon LaFell

    b. Ogemdi Nwagbuo

    c. DeAngelo Williams

    d. Greg Olsen

17. On March 30, 2012, the Carolina Panthers traded _____ to the Oakland Raiders for Bruce Campbell.

   a. Richie Brockel
   b. Mike Goodson
   c. Derek Anderson
   d. Jeremy Shockey

18. On October 4, 2013, the Carolina Panthers traded Jon Beason to the _____ for a 2014 7th round draft pick (Jabari Price).

   a. New York Giants
   b. Green Bay Packers
   c. Indianapolis Colts
   d. Arizona Cardinals

19. On September 28, 2015, the Carolina Panthers traded a 2016 6th round draft pick (Mike Thomas) to the Chicago Bears for _____.

   a. Ted Ginn Jr.
   b. Fozzy Whittaker
   c. Jared Allen
   d. Shaq Thompson

20. On March 24, 2020, the Carolina Panthers traded Cam Newton to the New England Patriots.

   a. True
   b. False

QUIZ ANSWERS

1. C – Pittsburgh Steelers

2. D – Oakland Raiders

3. A – True

4. B – Tyrone Poole

5. A – True

6. D – Tennessee Titans

7. C – Miami Dolphins

8. B – Todd Fordham

9. D – Denver Broncos

10. A – True

11. B – Chicago Bears

12. A – True

13. C – J.J. Jansen

14. A – True

15. A – Chicago Bears

16. D – Greg Olsen

17. B – Mike Goodson

18. A – New York Giants

19. C – Jared Allen

20. B – False (The Panthers cut Newton.)

DID YOU KNOW?

1. On August 29, 2016, the Carolina Panthers traded Kasey Redfern and a 2018 4th round draft pick (Durham Smythe) to the Cleveland Browns for Andy Lee and a 2017 7th round draft pick (Harrison Butker).

2. On September 3, 2017, the Carolina Panthers traded Kaelin Clay and a 2019 7th round draft pick (Tommy Sweeney) to the Buffalo Bills for Kevon Seymour.

3. On March 14, 2018, the Panthers traded Daryl Worley to the Philadelphia Eagles for Torrey Smith.

4. On September 25, 2018, the Panthers traded a 2021 conditional pick to the Buffalo Bills for Marshall Newhouse.

5. On March 4, 2020, the Panthers traded Trai Turner to the Los Angeles Chargers for Russell Okung.

6. On March 23, 2020, the Panthers traded Kyle Allen to the Washington Football Team for a 2020 5th round draft pick (Alton Robinson).

7. On August 31, 2020, the Panthers traded Andre Smith to the Buffalo Bills for a 2023 7th round draft pick.

8. On May 10, 2014, the Panthers traded a 2014 5th round draft pick (Marquis Spruill) and a 2014 7th round draft pick (Jabari Price) to the Minnesota Vikings for a 2014 5th round draft pick (Bene Benwikere).

9. On August 31, 2012, the Panthers traded a 2014 7th round draft pick (Kaleb Ramsay) to the San Francisco 49ers for Colin Jones.

10. On October 20, 2009, the Panthers traded a 2009 3rd round draft pick to the Kansas City Chiefs for Tank Tyler.

CHAPTER 8:

DRAFT DAY

QUIZ TIME!

1. Steve Smith was drafted by the Carolina Panthers in the
   _____ round of the 2001 NFL Draft.

   a. 2nd
   b. 3rd
   c. 4th
   d. 5th

2. With the 9th overall pick in the 1st round of the _____
   NFL Draft, the Panthers selected Luke Kuechly.

   a. 2009
   b. 2010
   c. 2011
   d. 2012

3. With the _____ overall pick in the 1st round of the 2002
   NFL Draft, the Panthers selected Julius Peppers.

   a. 1st
   b. 2nd

c. 3rd

d. 4th

4. With the _____ overall pick in 1st round of the 2003 NFL Draft, the Panthers selected Jordan Gross.

    a. 2nd

    b. 4th

    c. 8th

    d. 10th

5. With the 14th overall pick in the 1st round of the _____ NFL Draft, the Panthers selected Thomas Davis.

    a. 2005

    b. 2006

    c. 2007

    d. 2008

6. With the _____ overall pick in the 2nd round of the 1996 NFL Draft, the Panthers selected Muhsin Muhammad.

    a. 35th

    b. 38th

    c. 43rd

    d. 45th

7. With the 59th overall pick in the 2nd round of the 2007 NFL Draft, the Panthers selected Ryan Kalil.

    a. True

    b. False

8. With the 56th overall pick in the 2nd round of the _____ NFL Draft, the Panthers selected Mike Minter.

a. 1993
b. 1995
c. 1996
d. 1997

9. With the 38th overall pick in the 2nd round of the _____ NFL Draft, the Carolina Panthers selected Mike Rucker.

    a. 1995
    b. 1997
    c. 1999
    d. 2001

10. The Carolina Panthers drafted Chris Weinke in the 4th round, 106th overall in the 2001 NFL Draft.

    a. True
    b. False

11. With the 27th overall pick in the 1st round of the 2006 NFL Draft, the Panthers selected _____.

    a. Jake Delhomme
    b. DeAngelo Williams
    c. Drew Carter
    d. Keyshawn Johnson

12. Teddy Bridgewater was drafted in the 1st round, 32nd overall, of the 2014 NFL Draft by the Panthers.

    a. True
    b. False

13. With the 138th overall pick in the 5th round of the 2012 NFL Draft, the _____ selected Tahir Whitehead.

a. New York Giants

b. New Orleans Saints

c. Oakland Raiders

d. Detroit Lions

14. In the _____ round of the 2008 NFL Draft, the Panthers selected Jonathan Stewart.

    a. 8th

    b. 4th

    c. 2nd

    d. 1st

15. With the 98th overall pick in the 4th round of the 1991 NFL Draft, the _____ selected John Kasay.

    a. New Orleans Saints

    b. Seattle Seahawks

    c. Miami Dolphins

    d. San Diego Chargers

16. With the 141st overall pick in the 6th round of the 1989 NFL Draft, the _____ selected Rodney Peete.

    a. Detroit Lions

    b. Philadelphia Eagles

    c. Dallas Cowboys

    d. Washington Redskins

17. With the 44th overall pick in the 2nd round of the _____ NFL Draft, the Panthers selected Kris Jenkins.

    a. 1998

    b. 2000

c. 2001

d. 2003

18. Which team picked Greg Olsen in the 1st round, 31st overall in the 2007 NFL Draft?

   a. Seattle Seahawks

   b. Chicago Bears

   c. Miami Dolphins

   d. Pittsburgh Steelers

19. With the 13th overall pick in the 1st round of the 1989 NFL Draft, the _____ selected Eric Metcalf.

   a. Atlanta Falcons

   b. San Diego Chargers

   c. Cleveland Browns

   d. Arizona Cardinals

20. Kevin Greene was selected by the Los Angeles Rams in the 5th round, 113th overall in the 1985 NFL Draft.

   a. True

   b. False

QUIZ ANSWERS

1. B – 3rd

2. D – 2012

3. B – 2nd

4. C – 8th

5. A – 2005

6. C – 43rd

7. A – True

8. D – 1997

9. C – 1999

10. A – True

11. B – DeAngelo Williams

12. B – False (He was drafted by the Minnesota Vikings.)

13. D – Detroit Lions

14. D – 1st

15. B – Seattle Seahawks

16. A – Detroit Lions

17. C – 2001

18. B – Chicago Bears

19. C – Cleveland Browns

20. A – True

DID YOU KNOW?

1. Former Panther Chris Gamble was selected by the Carolina Panthers in the 1st round, 28th overall in the 2004 NFL Draft.

2. Former Panther David Carr was selected by the Houston Texans in the 1st round, 1st overall in the 2002 NFL Draft.

3. Former Panther Derek Anderson was selected by the Baltimore Ravens in the 6th round, 213th overall in the 2005 NFL Draft.

4. Former Panther Kerry Collins was selected by the Panthers in the 1st round, 5th overall in the 1995 NFL Draft.

5. Former Panther Eric Reid was selected by the San Francisco 49ers in the 1st round, 18th overall in the 2013 NFL Draft.

6. Current Panther Curtis Samuel was selected by the Panthers in the 2nd round, 40th overall in the 2017 NFL Draft.

7. Current Panther Christian McCaffrey was selected by the Panthers in the 1st round, 8th overall in the 2017 NFL Draft.

8. Current Panther D.J. Moore was selected by the Panthers in the 1st round, 24th overall in the 2018 NFL Draft.

9. Former Panther Ted Ginn Jr. was selected by the Miami Dolphins in the 1st round, 9th overall in the 2007 NFL Draft.

10. Former Panther Steve Beuerlein was selected by the Los Angeles Raiders in the 4th round, 110th overall in the 1987 NFL Draft.

CHAPTER 9:

ODDS & ENDS

QUIZ TIME!

1. DeAngelo Williams competed on _____ with Gary Barnidge and finished in fourth place.

    a. Big Brother
    b. The Amazing Race
    c. Survivor
    d. The Masked Singer

2. Chris Weinke spent six seasons in the Toronto Blue Jays' minor-league system before choosing to play football instead of baseball.

    a. True
    b. False

3. Rodney Peete is married to which actress?

    a. Halle Berry
    b. Vanessa Williams
    c. Holly Robinson
    d. Rosario Dawson

4. On June 4, 2020, Luke Kuechly returned to the Panthers as a _____.

    a. Special Assistant to the General Manager
    b. Linebacker Coach
    c. Executive Director of Football Staff
    d. Pro Scout

5. Which former baseball player was Ron Rivera's idol while he was growing up?

    a. Hank Aaron
    b. Willie Mays
    c. Roberto Clemente
    d. Jackie Robinson

6. In 2019, who played for the "home" team during the NBA All-Star Celebrity Game at the Bojangles Coliseum in Charlotte, North Carolina?

    a. Cam Newton
    b. Steve Smith
    c. Muhsin Muhammad
    d. Mike Minter

7. David Carr is the brother of current Las Vegas Raiders quarterback Derek Carr.

    a. True
    b. False

8. Who was the first Zairian to play in the National Football League?

    a. Muhsin Muhammad
    b. Kealoha Pilares

c. Tim Biakabutuka

d. Rocket Ismail

9. Where did John Fox attend college?

a. Stanford University

b. UC Berkeley

c. UC San Diego

d. San Diego State University

10. In high school, Graham Gano was a state title winner in which sport (other than football)?

a. Baseball

b. Tennis

c. Track & Field

d. Soccer

11. Who was drafted by the Detroit Tigers in the 26th round of the 1990 MLB Draft but opted to play football instead?

a. Mark Carrier

b. Kerry Collins

c. John Kasay

d. Sam Mills

12. Olindo Mare is mentioned in Wale's song "TV in the Radio" in the line "I kick it, kick it like Olindo."

a. True

b. False

13. Who was a Carolina Panthers offensive assistant from 2011 to 2012 and the Carolina Panthers wide receivers coach from 2013 to 2016?

a. Donald Hayes
b. Muhsin Muhammad
c. Steve Smith
d. Ricky Proehl

14. Who formerly co-hosted a morning show on Boston hip-hop radio station HOT 96.9?

    a. Jermaine Wiggins
    b. DeShaun Foster
    c. Brad Hoover
    d. Will Witherspoon

15. Whose father, Pedro Beltran, formerly pitched for the Atlanta Braves?

    a. Jason Baker
    b. Sherrod Martin
    c. Dante Rosario
    d. Captain Munnerlyn

16. The character Michael in the film *The Blind Side* starring Sandra Bullock is based on former Panther Mike Minter.

    a. True
    b. False

17. Who has appeared on two episodes of *Total Divas*, an E! Network TV show about WWE Divas, going on dates with Rosa Mendes and Summer Rae?

    a. Mike Tolbert
    b. Greg Olsen
    c. DeAngelo Williams
    d. Gary Barnidge

18. In the third season of the FXX TV series *The League*, the character Andre goes on a rant about which Panthers player?

    a. Gary Barnidge
    b. Brandon LaFell
    c. Mike Tolbert
    d. Charles Godfrey

19. While with the San Francisco 49ers, _____ decided to protest during the national anthem by taking a knee with Colin Kaepernick in the 2016 NFL season.

    a. Cameron Artis-Payne
    b. Ray-Ray McCloud
    c. Torrey Smith
    d. Eric Reid

20. Donte Curry is the brother of NBA star Stephen Curry.

    a. True
    b. False

QUIZ ANSWERS

1. B – The Amazing Race

2. A – True

3. C – Holly Robinson

4. D – Pro Scout

5. C – Roberto Clemente

6. B – Steve Smith

7. A – True

8. C – Tim Biakabutuka

9. D – San Diego State University

10. C – Track & Field

11. B – Kerry Collins

12. A – True

13. D – Ricky Proehl

14. A – Jermaine Wiggins

15. C – Dante Rosario

16. B – False (The character was based on Michael Oher.)

17. D – Gary Barnidge

18. C – Mike Tolbert

19. D – Eric Reid

20. B – False

DID YOU KNOW?

1. After retirement, Muhsin Muhammad became managing director at the private equity firm Axum Capital Partners, which he co-founded.

2. Christian McCaffrey has been in a relationship with fashion influencer and social media personality Olivia Culpo since 2019.

3. Thomas Davis recovered from three ACL tears in the same knee during his career, a feat no other professional athlete has accomplished.

4. Richie Cunningham was known during his NFL career for sharing his name with the *Happy Days* television character played by Ron Howard.

5. After retirement from the NFL, D.J. Hackett started a company that provides all-natural and organic foods to improve school nutrition.

6. D.J. Hackett appeared on the game show *Family Feud* with his family in April 2014.

7. After retiring from the NFL, Dwight Stone became an officer with the Charlotte Mecklenburg Police Department in Charlotte, NC. He served as both a school resource officer and patrol officer for 13 years.

8. Kevin Greene made several appearances in professional wrestling. He helped promote World Championship Wrestling in the 1990s.

9. When asked why his name is Captain, Captain Munnerlyn said, "My momma promised my grandmomma that she could name the last child. I was the boy of the family, and she named me Captain. Her great-grandfather was named Captain, so I got named after my great-great-grandfather. My sisters and brothers have normal names. I got the odd name. In the beginning it was kind of rough. Kids used to tease me a little, but it fits my personality, because I feel like I'm a leader."

10. Kyle Love was born in South Korea. His father was stationed there as an officer in the United States Army.

CHAPTER 10:

OFFENSE

QUIZ TIME!

1. How many Pro Bowls was Mike Tolbert named to during his 10-season NFL career?

    a. 0

    b. 2

    c. 3

    d. 5

2. Steve Smith played his entire 16-season NFL career with the Carolina Panthers.

    a. True

    b. False

3. During his 14-season NFL career, Muhsin Muhammad played for the Carolina Panthers and the _____.

    a. San Francisco 49ers

    b. Oakland Raiders

    c. Buffalo Bills

    d. Chicago Bears

4. Greg Olsen spent nine seasons of his NFL career with the Carolina Panthers.

    a. True

    b. False

5. How many seasons did Rodney Peete spend with the Carolina Panthers?

    a. 1

    b. 2

    c. 3

    d. 4

6. How many touchdowns did Jonathan Stewart record during his 2008 rookie season with the Panthers?

    a. 3

    b. 7

    c. 10

    d. 11

7. Tim Biakabutuka played his entire six-season NFL career with the Panthers.

    a. True

    b. False

8. Which of the following teams did former Panther Jake Delhomme NOT play for during his 11 seasons in the NFL?

    a. New Orleans Saints

    b. Indianapolis Colts

    c. Cleveland Browns

    d. Houston Texans

9. How many seasons did Matt Moore play for the Panthers?

    a. 1

    b. 2

    c. 3

    d. 5

10. How many seasons did Cam Newton play for the Panthers?

    a. 5

    b. 6

    c. 8

    d. 9

11. How many Super Bowls did Torrey Smith win during his eight-season NFL career?

    a. 0

    b. 1

    c. 2

    d. 3

12. Brad Hoover spent his entire nine-season NFL career with the Panthers.

    a. True

    b. False

13. How many Pro Bowls was Stephen Davis named to during his 11-season NFL career?

    a. 0

    b. 1

    c. 2

    d. 3

14. How many seasons did Fozzy Whittaker play for the Panthers?

    a. 2
    b. 4
    c. 5
    d. 6

15. During his nine-year NFL career, Brandon LaFell played for the Carolina Panthers, Cincinnati Bengals, Oakland Raiders, and the _____.

    a. New England Patriots
    b. Dallas Cowboys
    c. Seattle Seahawks
    d. New York Jets

16. How many Pro Bowls was Kerry Collins named to during his 18 seasons in the NFL?

    a. 1
    b. 2
    c. 6
    d. 9

17. During his eight-season NFL career, Gary Barnidge played for the Carolina Panthers and the _____.

    a. Pittsburgh Steelers
    b. New York Giants
    c. Cleveland Browns
    d. New England Patriots

18. Which of the following teams did former Panther Wesley Walls NOT play for during his 14-season NFL career?

    a. San Francisco 49ers
    b. New Orleans Saints
    c. Green Bay Packers
    d. Minnesota Vikings

19. Which of the following teams did former Panther David Carr NOT play for during his 10-season NFL career?

    a. Houston Texans
    b. Oakland Raiders
    c. New York Giants
    d. San Francisco 49ers

20. During his 21-season NFL career, Vinny Testaverde was named to two Pro Bowls.

    a. True
    b. False

QUIZ ANSWERS

1. C – 3

2. B – False (He played for the Panthers and Baltimore Ravens.)

3. D – Chicago Bears

4. A – True

5. C – 3

6. C – 10

7. A – True

8. B – Indianapolis Colts

9. C – 3

10. D – 9

11. C – 2

12. A – True

13. D – 3

14. B – 4

15. A – New England Patriots

16. B – 2

17. C – Cleveland Browns

18. D – Minnesota Vikings

19. B – Oakland Raiders

20. A – True

DID YOU KNOW?

1. Cam Newton played nine seasons for the Carolina Panthers and is currently with the New England Patriots. He played 125 games with the Panthers and is a three-time Pro Bowler, one-time All-Pro, one-time MVP, 2011 Offensive Rookie of the Year, 2015 Offensive Player of the Year, and 2015 Bert Bell Award winner.

2. Steve Smith spent 13 seasons of his 16-season NFL career with the Panthers. He also played for the Baltimore Ravens. He is a five-time Pro Bowler, two-time All-Pro, and 2005 Comeback Player of the Year Award winner.

3. Jonathan Stewart spent 10 of his 11 NFL seasons with the Panthers. He also played for the New York Giants. He is a one-time Pro Bowler.

4. Mike Tolbert spent five seasons of his 10-season NFL career with the Panthers. He also played for the San Diego Chargers and Buffalo Bills. He is a three-time Pro Bowler and two-time All-Pro.

5. Rodney Peete spent three of his 15 NFL seasons with the Panthers. He also played for the Detroit Lions, Philadelphia Eagles, Dallas Cowboys, Oakland Raiders, and Washington Redskins.

6. Muhsin Muhammad spent 11 seasons of his 14-season NFL career with the Carolina Panthers. He also played for

the Chicago Bears. He is a two-time Pro Bowler and one-time All-Pro.

7. Greg Olsen spent nine seasons with the Panthers. He has also played for the Chicago Bears, and he is currently with the Seattle Seahawks. He is a three-time Pro Bowler so far.

8. Mark Carrier spent four seasons of his 12-season NFL career with the Panthers. He also played for the Tampa Bay Buccaneers and Cleveland Browns. He is a one-time Pro Bowler.

9. Stephen Davis spent three seasons of his 11-season NFL career with the Panthers. He also played for the Washington Redskins and St. Louis Rams. He is a three-time Pro Bowler.

10. Jake Delhomme spent seven seasons of his 11-season NFL career with the Panthers. He also played for the New Orleans Saints, Cleveland Browns, and Houston Texans. He is a one-time Pro Bowler.

CHAPTER 11:

DEFENSE

QUIZ TIME!

1. How many Pro Bowls was Luke Kuechly named to during his eight-season NFL career?

   a. 4
   b. 5
   c. 6
   d. 7

2. Luke Kuechly played his entire eight-season NFL career with the Carolina Panthers.

   a. True
   b. False

3. What year was Reggie White inducted into the Pro Football Hall of Fame?

   a. 2002
   b. 2004
   c. 2006
   d. 2008

4. During his 17-season NFL career, Julius Peppers played for the Carolina Panthers, Chicago Bears, and the _____.

   a. San Francisco 49ers
   b. Green Bay Packers
   c. Dallas Cowboys
   d. New England Patriots

5. During his 12-season NFL career, Sam Mills played for the Carolina Panthers and the _____.

   a. Philadelphia Eagles
   b. Arizona Cardinals
   c. Jacksonville Jaguars
   d. New Orleans Saints

6. How many seasons did Josh Norman play for the Panthers?

   a. 2
   b. 3
   c. 4
   d. 5

7. Mike Minter played his entire 10-season NFL career with the Panthers.

   a. True
   b. False

8. What year was Kevin Greene inducted into the Pro Football Hall of Fame?

   a. 2015
   b. 2016

c. 2017

d. 2018

9. How many seasons has Thomas Davis spent with the Panthers (as of the 2020 season)?

a. 9

b. 10

c. 13

d. 15

10. How many Pro Bowls was Jon Beason named to during his 10-season NFL career?

a. 1

b. 3

c. 4

d. 5

11. In his seven-season NFL career, Eric Reid played for the Carolina Panthers and the _____.

a. Denver Broncos

b. Tennessee Titans

c. Baltimore Ravens

d. San Francisco 49ers

12. Jordan Gross played his entire 11-season NFL career with the Panthers.

a. True

b. False

13. Which of the following teams did former Panther James Anderson NOT play for?

a. Chicago Bears

b. New Orleans Saints

c. Kansas City Chiefs

d. Tennessee Titans

14. During his 10-season NFL career, Captain Munnerlyn played for the Carolina Panthers and the _____.

a. Minnesota Vikings

b. Atlanta Falcons

c. Denver Broncos

d. Oakland Raiders

15. How many seasons did Mario Addison spend with the Panthers?

a. 7

b. 8

c. 9

d. 10

16. Mike Rucker spent his entire nine-season NFL career with the Carolina Panthers.

a. True

b. False

17. How many Pro Bowls was Jared Allen named to during his 13-season NFL career?

a. 0

b. 2

c. 4

d. 5

18. Charles Tillman spent one season with the Carolina Panthers and 12 seasons with which team?

    a. Baltimore Ravens
    b. Pittsburgh Steelers
    c. Chicago Bears
    d. Seattle Seahawks

19. How many seasons did Sean Gilbert spend with the Carolina Panthers in his 11 NFL seasons?

    a. 2
    b. 3
    c. 4
    d. 5

20. Charles Johnson spent his entire 11-season NFL career with the Carolina Panthers.

    a. True
    b. False

QUIZ ANSWERS

1. D – 7

2. A – True

3. C – 2006

4. B – Green Bay Packers

5. D – New Orleans Saints

6. C – 4

7. A – True

8. B – 2016

9. C – 13

10. B – 3

11. D – San Francisco 49ers

12. A – True

13. C – Kansas City Chiefs

14. A – Minnesota Vikings

15. B – 8

16. A – True

17. D – 5

18. C – Chicago Bears

19. D – 5

20. A – True

DID YOU KNOW?

1. Julius Peppers spent 10 seasons of his 17-season NFL career with the Carolina Panthers. He also played for the Chicago Bears and Green Bay Packers. He is a nine-time Pro Bowler, three-time All-Pro, 2002 Defensive Rookie of the Year, member of the HOF All-2000s team, and member of the HOF All-2010s team.

2. Luke Kuechly spent his entire eight-season NFL career with the Carolina Panthers. He is a seven-time Pro Bowler, five-time All-Pro, 2012 Defensive Rookie of the Year, 2013 Defensive Player of the Year, and member of the HOF All-2010s team.

3. Jordan Gross spent his entire 11-season NFL career with the Panthers. He is a three-time Pro Bowler and one-time All-Pro.

4. Kevin Greene spent three of his 15 NFL seasons with the Panthers. He also played for the St. Louis Rams, Pittsburgh Steelers, and San Francisco 49ers. He was a five-time Pro Bowler, two-time All-Pro, member of the HOF All-1990s team, and member of the Pro Football Hall of Fame.

5. Thomas Davis spent 13 seasons with the Carolina Panthers. He has also played for the Los Angeles Chargers, and he is currently with the Washington

Football Team. So far, he is a three-time Pro Bowler, one-time All-Pro, and 2014 Walter Payton Award winner.

6. Sam Mills spent three seasons of his 12-season NFL career with the Panthers. He also played for the New Orleans Saints. He was a five-time Pro Bowler and one-time All-Pro.

7. Reggie White spent just one of his 15 NFL seasons with the Panthers. He also played for the Philadelphia Eagles and Green Bay Packers. He was a thirteen-time Pro Bowler, eight-time All-Pro, one-time Super Bowl champion, 1987 and 1998 Defensive Player of the Year, member of the HOF All-1980s and All-1990s teams, and member of the Pro Football Hall of Fame.

8. Mike Rucker spent his entire nine-season NFL career with the Carolina Panthers. He is a one-time Pro Bowler.

9. Josh Norman spent four seasons of his NFL career with the Carolina Panthers. He has also played for the Washington Redskins, and he is currently with the Buffalo Bills. So far, he is a one-time Pro Bowler and a one-time All-Pro.

10. Jon Beason spent seven seasons of his 10-season NFL career with the Panthers. He also played for the New York Giants. He is a three-time Pro Bowler and one-time All-Pro.

CHAPTER 12:

SPECIAL TEAMS

QUIZ TIME!

1. During his 20-season NFL career, John Kasay played for the Carolina Panthers, New Orleans Saints, and the

   _____.

   a. Cincinnati Bengals
   b. Green Bay Packers
   c. Denver Broncos
   d. Seattle Seahawks

2. John Kasay was named to only one Pro Bowl in his 20-season NFL career.

   a. True
   b. False

3. How many seasons did Graham Gano play for the Carolina Panthers?

   a. 2
   b. 4
   c. 7
   d. 9

4. Which of the following teams did Olindo Mare NOT play for?

    a. Miami Dolphins

    b. Oakland Raiders

    c. Seattle Seahawks

    d. Chicago Bears

5. How many seasons did Jason Baker play for the Panthers?

    a. 4

    b. 5

    c. 6

    d. 7

6. How many NFL teams did Shayne Graham play for during his 17-season NFL career?

    a. 3

    b. 4

    c. 10

    d. 12

7. As of the 2020 season, Andy Lee has played for the Panthers, San Francisco 49ers, Cleveland Browns, and Arizona Cardinals.

    a. True

    b. False

8. During his five-season NFL career, Michael Palardy played for the Carolina Panthers and the _____.

    a. Denver Broncos

    b. Oakland Raiders

c. New York Giants

d. New York Jets

9. Which of these teams did Tommy Barnhardt NOT play for in his 15-season NFL career?

a. New Orleans Saints

b. Tampa Bay Buccaneers

c. New England Patriots

d. Washington Redskins

10. How many Pro Bowls was Rohn Stark named to during his 16-season NFL career?

a. 1

b. 2

c. 3

d. 4

11. How many Super Bowl championships did Ken Walter win during his nine-season NFL career?

a. 0

b. 1

c. 2

d. 3

12. Richie Cunningham was never named to a Pro Bowl during his six-season NFL career.

a. True

b. False

13. Which of the following teams did Joe Nedney NOT play for during his 16-season NFL career?

a. Pittsburgh Steelers

b. San Francisco 49ers

c. Arizona Cardinals

d. Denver Broncos

14. Which of these teams did Todd Sauerbrun NOT play for in his 13-season NFL career?

a. Chicago Bears

b. Denver Broncos

c. Atlanta Falcons

d. New England Patriots

15. Rhys Lloyd played four seasons with the Carolina Panthers and one season with which team?

a. Dallas Cowboys

b. Minnesota Vikings

c. Detroit Lions

d. Baltimore Ravens

16. Todd Carter only played one season in the NFL, 2010 with the Carolina Panthers.

a. True

b. False

17. During his six-season NFL career, Brad Nortman played for the Carolina Panthers and the _____.

a. Philadelphia Eagles

b. Indianapolis Colts

c. Jacksonville Jaguars

d. New England Patriots

18. Justin Medlock played two seasons in the NFL, one with the Carolina Panthers and one with which team?

  a. Houston Texans
  b. Kansas City Chiefs
  c. San Diego Chargers
  d. St. Louis Rams

19. Which of the following teams did Chandler Catanzaro NOT play for in his six-season NFL career?

  a. Arizona Cardinals
  b. New York Jets
  c. Tampa Bay Buccaneers
  d. Los Angeles Chargers

20. Current Carolina Panthers kicker Joey Slye has been with the team since 2019.

  a. True
  b. False

QUIZ ANSWERS

1. D – Seattle Seahawks

2. A – True

3. C – 7

4. B – Oakland Raiders

5. D – 7

6. C – 10

7. A – True

8. B – Oakland Raiders

9. C – New England Patriots

10. D – 4

11. C – 2

12. B – False (He was named to one Pro Bowl.)

13. A – Pittsburgh Steelers

14. C – Atlanta Falcons

15. D – Baltimore Ravens

16. A – True

17. C – Jacksonville Jaguars

18. B – Kansas City Chiefs

19. D – Los Angeles Chargers

20. A – True

DID YOU KNOW?

1. John Kasay spent 15 of his 20 NFL seasons with the Panthers. He also played for the Seattle Seahawks and New Orleans Saints. He is a one-time Pro Bowler.

2. Olindo Mare spent one of his 16 NFL seasons with the Carolina Panthers. He also played for the Miami Dolphins, Seattle Seahawks, Chicago Bears, and New Orleans Saints. He is a one-time Pro Bowler and one-time All-Pro.

3. Andy Lee spent one season with the Carolina Panthers. He has also played for the San Francisco 49ers and Cleveland Browns, and he currently plays for the Arizona Cardinals. So far, he is a three-time Pro Bowler and three-time All-Pro.

4. Graham Gano spent seven seasons with the Carolina Panthers, and he has also played for the Washington Redskins. He currently plays for the New York Giants. So far, he is a one-time Pro Bowler.

5. Jason Baker spent seven seasons of his 14-season NFL career with the Panthers. He also played for the Kansas City Chiefs, San Francisco 49ers, Denver Broncos, Indianapolis Colts, and Philadelphia Eagles.

6. Joe Nedney spent one season of his 16 NFL seasons with the Carolina Panthers. He also played for the San

Francisco 49ers, Arizona Cardinals, Tennessee Titans, Denver Broncos, Miami Dolphins, and Oakland Raiders.

7. Ken Walter spent four seasons of his nine-season NFL career with the Panthers. He also played for the Seattle Seahawks and New England Patriots. He is a two-time Super Bowl champion.

8. Brad Nortman spent four seasons of his six-season NFL career with the Carolina Panthers. He also played for the Jacksonville Jaguars.

9. 9 Todd Sauerbrun spent four seasons of his 13-season NFL career with the Carolina Panthers. He also played for the Chicago Bears, Denver Broncos, Kansas City Chiefs, and New England Patriots. He is a three-time Pro Bowler and two-time All-Pro.

10. 10. Rohn Stark spent one season of his 16-season NFL career with the Panthers. He also played for the Indianapolis Colts, Pittsburgh Steelers, and Seattle Seahawks. He is a four-time Pro Bowler and one-time All-Pro.

CHAPTER 13:

SUPER BOWL

QUIZ TIME!

1. How many Super Bowls have the Carolina Panthers won?

    a. 0

    b. 1

    c. 2

    d. 3

2. How many NFC championships have the Carolina Panthers won (as of the end of the 2020 season)?

    a. 1

    b. 2

    c. 3

    d. 4

3. Which team did the Carolina Panthers face in Super Bowl XXXVIII?

    a. Pittsburgh Steelers

    b. Baltimore Ravens

    c. New England Patriots

    d. Denver Broncos

4. Which team did the Carolina Panthers face in Super Bowl 50?

    a. Indianapolis Colts
    b. Tennessee Titans
    c. Pittsburgh Steelers
    d. Denver Broncos

5. How many NFC South division championships have the Carolina Panthers won (as of the end of the 2020 season)?

    a. 4
    b. 5
    c. 6
    d. 7

6. How many appearances have the Carolina Panthers made in the NFL playoffs (as of the end of the 2020 season)?

    a. 4
    b. 6
    c. 8
    d. 10

7. Super Bowl 50 was played at Levi's Stadium in Santa Clara, California, home of the San Francisco 49ers.

    a. True
    b. False

8. Where was Super Bowl XXXVIII played?

    a. Qualcomm Stadium in San Diego, California
    b. Ford Field in Detroit, Michigan
    c. Alltel Stadium in Jacksonville, Florida
    d. Reliant Stadium in Houston, Texas

9. Who sang the national anthem at Super Bowl 50?

   a. Idina Menzel
   b. Pink
   c. Lady Gaga
   d. Alicia Keys

10. Who sang the national anthem at Super Bowl XXXVIII?

    a. Dixie Chicks
    b. Beyoncé
    c. Mariah Carey
    d. Billy Joel

11. Who was the Carolina Panthers' head coach for Super Bowl XXXVIII?

    a. John Fox
    b. Ron Rivera
    c. Dom Capers
    d. George Seifert

12. Ron Rivera was the Carolina Panthers' head coach for Super Bowl 50.

    a. True
    b. False

13. Who played the halftime show at Super Bowl XXXVIII?

    a. Paul McCartney
    b. Prince
    c. Jessica Simpson, Ocean of Soul, Spirit of Houston, Janet Jackson, Justin Timberlake, P. Diddy, Kid Rock, and Nelly
    d. The Rolling Stones

14. Who played the halftime show at Super Bowl 50?

    a. Justin Timberlake
    b. Coldplay featuring Beyoncé and Bruno Mars with Mark Ronson
    c. Lady Gaga
    d. Maroon 5

15. What was the final score of Super Bowl 50?

    a. Broncos 52, Panthers 17
    b. Broncos 24, Panthers 17
    c. Broncos 24, Panthers 10
    d. Broncos 31, Panthers 10

16. The final score of Super Bowl XXXVIII was Patriots 32, Panthers 29.

    a. True
    b. False

17. Who was the Panthers' starting quarterback in Super Bowl XXXVIII?

    a. Rodney Peete
    b. Jake Delhomme
    c. Todd Sauerbrun
    d. Kerry Collins

18. Who was the Panthers' starting quarterback in Super Bowl 50?

    a. Teddy Bridgewater
    b. Christian McCaffrey
    c. Derek Anderson
    d. Cam Newton

19. How much did a 30-second commercial cost during Super Bowl XXXVIII?

    a. $500,000
    b. $1.1 million
    c. $2.2 million
    d. $3.3 million

20. A 30-second commercial during Super Bowl 50 cost $5.01 million.

    a. True
    b. False

QUIZ ANSWERS

1. A – 0

2. B – 2 (2003, 2015)

3. C – New England Patriots

4. D – Denver Broncos

5. B – 5

6. C – 8

7. A – True

8. D – Reliant Stadium in Houston, Texas

9. C – Lady Gaga

10. B – Beyoncé

11. A – John Fox

12. A – True

13. C – Jessica Simpson, Ocean of Soul, Spirit of Houston, Janet Jackson, Justin Timberlake, P. Diddy, Kid Rock, and Nelly

14. B – Coldplay featuring Beyoncé and Bruno Mars with Mark Ronson

15. C – Broncos 24, Panthers 10

16. A – True

17. B – Jake Delhomme

18. D – Cam Newton

19. C – $2.2 million

20. A – True

DID YOU KNOW?

1. Janet Jackson had her infamous "wardrobe malfunction" with Justin Timberlake during the halftime show at Super Bowl XXXVIII.

2. Super Bowl XXXVIII set the record for most Roman numerals in a Super Bowl title (7). This will not occur again until 2043.

3. The broadcast of Super Bowl 50 was the third most-watched program in American TV history with an average of 111.9 million viewers. It remains the highest-rated program in the history of CBS.

4. Super Bowl 50 was the final game of Peyton Manning's NFL career.

5. Super Bowl 50 was the first Super Bowl held in the Bay Area since Super Bowl XIX in 1985 and the first in California since Super Bowl XXXVII took place in San Diego in 2003.

6. Super Bowl 50 marked the third straight season that the number one seeds in the NFC and AFC met in the Super Bowl.

7. During Super Bowl 50, the Panthers used the San Jose State University practice facility and stayed at the San Jose Marriott.

8. *Sports Illustrated* writer Peter King hailed Super Bowl XXXVIII as the "Greatest Super Bowl of all time."

9. Super Bowl XXXVIII was played on February 1, 2004.

10. Super Bowl 50 was played on February 7, 2016.

CHAPTER 14:

HEATED RIVALRIES

QUIZ TIME!

1. Which team does NOT play in the NFC South with the Panthers?

    a. New Orleans Saints

    b. Atlanta Falcons

    c. Tampa Bay Buccaneers

    d. Indianapolis Colts

2. Before the 2002 season, the Tampa Bay Buccaneers were in the AFC West and NFC Central while the Panthers, Saints, and Falcons were part of the NFC West.

    a. True

    b. False

3. The Panthers currently have not won a Super Bowl. How many have the Atlanta Falcons won?

    a. 0

    b. 1

    c. 2

    d. 3

4. The Panthers currently have not won a Super Bowl. How many have the Tampa Bay Buccaneers won?

    a. 0
    b. 1
    c. 2
    d. 3

5. The Panthers currently have not won a Super Bowl. How many have the New Orleans Saints won?

    a. 0
    b. 1
    c. 2
    d. 3

6. The Carolina Panthers have five NFC South division titles. How many do the Atlanta Falcons have?

    a. 1
    b. 2
    c. 3
    d. 4

7. The Carolina Panthers have won the most NFC South titles of any team in the division.

    a. True
    b. False

8. The Carolina Panthers have won five NFC South division titles. How many have the Tampa Bay Buccaneers won?

    a. 1
    b. 2

c. 3

d. 4

9. What is the Panthers' longest win streak versus the Falcons?

    a. 1

    b. 2

    c. 3

    d. 4

10. What is the Falcons' longest win streak versus the Panthers?

    a. 2

    b. 3

    c. 5

    d. 6

11. The very first game between the Panthers and Falcons took place in _____.

    a. 1995

    b. 1998

    c. 2000

    d. 2003

12. The Carolina Panthers and Tampa Bay Buccaneers have never met in the playoffs.

    a. True

    b. False

13. What is the Panthers' longest win streak versus the Buccaneers?

a. 4

b. 6

c. 8

d. 9

14. What is the name of the rivalry between the Panthers and the Atlanta Falcons?

    a. Georgia-Carolina Rivalry

    b. Cat Bird Rivalry

    c. I-85 Rivalry

    d. Battle of I-85

15. The Carolina Panthers have won seven playoff berths. How many have the Atlanta Falcons won?

    a. 2

    b. 4

    c. 6

    d. 8

16. The Carolina Panthers have won seven playoff berths, and the New Orleans Saints have won nine.

    a. True

    b. False

17. The Carolina Panthers have won seven playoff berths. How many have the Tampa Bay Buccaneers won?

    a. 2

    b. 4

    c. 6

    d. 7

18. In the 2017 NFL season, the NFC South had three teams qualify for the playoffs. Which team did NOT make it to the playoffs that year?

    a. Carolina Panthers
    b. Atlanta Falcons
    c. Tampa Bay Buccaneers
    d. New Orleans Saints

19. In 2014, the Carolina Panthers became the second team in NFL history to win its division and advance to the playoffs with a losing record (7-8-1).

    a. True
    b. False

20. From 2002 to 2009, no team in the NFC South earned back-to-back playoff appearances.

    a. True
    b. False

QUIZ ANSWERS

1. D – Indianapolis Colts

2. A – True

3. A – 0

4. B – 1

5. B – 1

6. D – 4

7. B – False (The New Orleans Saints have won seven.)

8. C – 3

9. C – 3

10. D – 6

11. A – 1995

12. A – True

13. B – 6

14. C – I-85 Rivalry

15. D – 8

16. A – True

17. B – 4

18. C – Tampa Bay Buccaneers

19. A – True

20. A – True

DID YOU KNOW?

1. The NFC South is the only NFC division that does not include any teams that predate the 1960 launch of the American Football League (AFL).

2. Both the Panthers and the Atlanta Falcons lost their two Super Bowls to the same two AFC teams: the Denver Broncos and the New England Patriots.

3. The Panthers were the first team to repeat as NFC South champions. They were also the first team to win the division title three years in a row.

4. On January 7, 2018, two NFC South teams, the Carolina Panthers and New Orleans Saints, met in the NFL playoffs for the first time since the division's creation in 2002. Before then, they were the only division left in the NFL who had never had teams face off against each other in the postseason.

5. Each NFC South team has won the division at least three times and made a playoff appearance at least three times since the division was formed.

6. The NFC South is the only NFL division where no team has swept the division during a regular season.

7. The Carolina Panthers have the best playoff record (9-8) of any team in the NFC South. They are also the only team in the NFC South that does not currently have a losing

playoff record. The New Orleans Saints' playoff record is 9-12, the Atlanta Falcons' playoff record is 10-14, and the Tampa Bay Buccaneers' playoff record is 6-9.

8. Since 2002, each NFC South team has won at least three division titles, the only current division in the NFL to achieve this feat.

9. The Carolina Panthers won the NFC West division title in 1996. They were in the NFC West from 1995 through 2001. They moved to the NFC South in 2002.

10. While the Carolina Panthers were in the NFC West, they began developing a rivalry with the San Francisco 49ers, but it became obsolete when the Panthers moved to the NFC South.

CHAPTER 15:

THE AWARDS SECTION

QUIZ TIME!

1. Which Panther won the 2015 MVP Award?

    a. Greg Olsen
    b. Cam Newton
    c. Luke Kuechly
    d. Fozzy Whittaker

2. Steve Smith was named the 2005 AP Comeback Player of the Year.

    a. True
    b. False

3. Who was named the 2012 AP Defensive Rookie of the Year?

    a. Thomas Davis
    b. Greg Hardy
    c. Luke Kuechly
    d. Josh Norman

4. Who was named the 2002 AP Defensive Rookie of the Year?

   a. Mike Rucker
   b. Mike Minter
   c. Mark Fields
   d. Julius Peppers

5. Who won the 2014 Walter Payton Man of the Year Award?

   a. Cam Newton
   b. Thomas Davis
   c. Tre Boston
   d. Roman Harper

6. Ron Rivera was named the NFL Coach of the Year in _____ and 2015.

   a. 2011
   b. 2012
   c. 2013
   d. 2014

7. Christian McCaffrey was named the 2019 DraftKings Daily Fantasy Player of the Year.

   a. True
   b. False

8. Which Panther won the 2017 Art Rooney Sportsmanship Award?

   a. Graham Gano
   b. Greg Olsen
   c. Jonathan Stewart
   d. Luke Kuechly

9. Cam Newton was named the _____ AP Offensive Rookie of the Year and the _____ AP Offensive Player of the Year.

    a. 2012, 2016
    b. 2011, 2015
    c. 2011, 2014
    d. 2012, 2013

10. In 2005, who earned the NFL's receiving "triple crown," leading the league in receptions (103), yards (1,563), and touchdowns (12)?

    a. Keary Colbert
    b. DeShaun Foster
    c. Steve Smith
    d. Chris Weinke

11. Wesley Walls was inducted into the College Football Hall of Fame in what year?

    a. 2010
    b. 2012
    c. 2014
    d. 2016

12. Luke Kuechly was the youngest recipient of the AP NFL Defensive Player of the Year Award in the history of the award.

    a. True
    b. False

13. In _____, Rodney Peete was inducted into the Arizona Sports Hall of Fame.

    a. 2006
    b. 2007
    c. 2009
    d. 2012

14. Which former Panther won the 2018 Panthers Ed Block Courage Award?

    a. Cam Newton
    b. Torrey Smith
    c. Julius Peppers
    d. Greg Olsen

15. Which Panther won the 2016 ESPY Award for Best NFL Player?

    a. Ted Ginn Jr.
    b. Cam Newton
    c. Luke Kuechly
    d. Thomas Davis

16. Jordan Gross was an Outland Trophy finalist in 2002.

    a. True
    b. False

17. Who won the 2006 Morris Trophy?

    a. Mike Minter
    b. Jake Delhomme
    c. Ryan Kalil
    d. Jordan Gross

18. Which Panther won the Glenn Davis Award in 1997?

    a. Todd Sauerbrun
    b. Chris Weinke
    c. Steve Beuerlein
    d. DeShaun Foster

19. Which of the following celebrities has NOT hosted the NFL Honors Awards Show (as of the 2019 season)?

    a. Alec Baldwin
    b. Jimmy Fallon
    c. Seth Meyers
    d. Steve Harvey

20. Chris Weinke won the Heisman Trophy in 2000.

    a. True
    b. False

QUIZ ANSWERS

1. B – Cam Newton

2. A – True

3. C – Luke Kuechly

4. D – Julius Peppers

5. B – Thomas Davis

6. C – 2013

7. A – True

8. D – Luke Kuechly

9. B – 2011, 2015

10. C – Steve Smith

11. C – 2014

12. A – True

13. D – 2012

14. C – Julius Peppers

15. B – Cam Newton

16. A – True

17. C – Ryan Kalil

18. D – DeShaun Foster

19. B – Jimmy Fallon

20. A – True

DID YOU KNOW?

1. Cam Newton won the Bert Bell Award in 2015. He had been named the Pepsi NFL Rookie of the Year in 2011.

2. Each year, CEO Inc. presents the Carolina Panthers Community Impact Player of the Year Award. Winners have been Thomas Davis (2016), Greg Olsen (2017), Kawann Short (2018), and Cam Newton (2019).

3. The Carolina Panthers presented Muhsin Muhammad with their Man of the Year Award in 1999 for his charity and volunteer work. He also won a Chicago Emmy Award for Outstanding Achievement for Sports Programs.

4. The NFL hosts an NFL honors show each year to give out awards such as MVP, Rookie of the Year, and Coach of the Year. NFL Honors debuted in Indianapolis in 2012. It is hosted in the city that is hosting the Super Bowl and on the network that is carrying that year's championship game.

5. The Carolina Panthers' Hall of Honor has enshrined Mike McCormack, Sam Mills, PSL Owners, Steve Smith, Jake Delhomme, Wesley Walls, and Jordan Gross.

6. Cam Newton won the King of Swag Award at the 2016 Kids' Choice Sports Awards.

7. Carolina Panthers Ed Block Courage Award winners have been Brett Maxie, Lamar Lathon, Tshimanga Biakabutuka, Steve Beuerlein, Mike Minter, Muhsin Muhammad,

Patrick Jeffers, Kevin Donnalley, DeShaun Foster, Mark Fields, Steve Smith, Colin Branch, Mike Rucker, Jake Delhomme, Dan Connor, Jordan Gross, Thomas Davis, Ron Edwards, Ryan Kalil, Greg Olsen, Cam Newton, Luke Kuechly, Graham Gano, Julius Peppers, and Shaq Thompson.

8. While in college, Chris Weinke won both the Davey O'Brien Award and the Johnny Unitas Award in 2000.

9. Todd Sauerbrun won the 2001 PFW Golden Toe Award.

10. Jonathan Stewart was named the 2007 Sun Bowl MVP while a member of the Oregon Ducks.

CHAPTER 16:

THE QUEEN CITY

QUIZ TIME!

1. The Charlotte Metropolitan area is the largest in the United States without a _____.

    a. MLB stadium
    b. Museum
    c. Zoo
    d. Amusement park

2. The Charlotte Motor Speedway holds three of NASCAR's biggest annual events: The Coca-Cola 600, the Bank of America 500, and the NASCAR Sprint All-Star Race.

    a. True
    b. False

3. The first _____ store opened in Charlotte, North Carolina.

    a. Trader Joe's
    b. Family Dollar
    c. Walmart
    d. Macy's

4. Which celebrity is NOT from Charlotte, North Carolina?

    a. Stephen Curry
    b. Dwayne "The Rock" Johnson
    c. Jeff Gordon
    d. Jennifer Aniston

5. North Carolina's oldest _____ is located in Charlotte and has been named a historic landmark.

    a. McDonald's
    b. Post office
    c. Dairy Queen
    d. City hall

6. Which company is NOT based in Charlotte?

    a. Bank of America
    b. Nike
    c. Honeywell
    d. Lowe's

7. Charlotte is the largest city in the state of North Carolina.

    a. True
    b. False

8. Which movie filmed a scene in Charlotte at the Knight Theater?

    a. Twilight
    b. The Wolf of Wall Street
    c. Moneyball
    d. The Hunger Games

9. What is the name of Charlotte's NBA team?

    a. Charlotte Pistons
    b. Charlotte Cubs
    c. Charlotte Hornets
    d. Charlotte Warriors

10. What was the name of Charlotte's former WNBA team?

    a. Charlotte Comets
    b. Charlotte Sting
    c. Charlotte Sparks
    d. Charlotte Liberty

11. What is the name of the Hornets' arena?

    a. Chase Center
    b. Spectrum Center
    c. American Airlines Center
    d. Wells Fargo Center

12. North Carolina has an NHL team, the Carolina Hurricanes, which plays in nearby Raleigh.

    a. True
    b. False

13. What is the name of the brand-new MLS team in Charlotte?

    a. Charlotte Galaxy
    b. Charlotte Shamrocks
    c. Charlotte Murder Hornets
    d. Charlotte FC

14. What is the name of Charlotte's MLB team?

    a. Charlotte Cubs

    b. Charlotte Athletics

    c. Charlotte Cardinals

    d. Charlotte does not have an MLB team.

15. What is the name of the top-ranked children's museum in America, located in Charlotte?

    a. The Strong Museum

    b. Port Discovery Children's Museum

    c. Imaginon

    d. Please Touch Museum

16. The U.S. National Whitewater Center, on the outskirts of Charlotte, has the world's largest manmade whitewater river.

    a. True

    b. False

17. Charlotte is home to the _____ Hall of Fame.

    a. Pro Football

    b. NASCAR

    c. National Baseball

    d. Hockey

18. What is Charlotte Douglas International Airport's code?

    a. CLT

    b. CDI

    c. CNC

    d. CIA

19. Charlotte is the _____ cheese capital of the world.

    a. Asiago

    b. Parmesan

    c. Gouda

    d. Pimento

20. *Talladega Nights: The Ballad of Ricky Bobby*, starring Will Ferrell, was shot on location in Charlotte.

    a. True

    b. False

QUIZ ANSWERS

1. C – Zoo

2. A – True

3. B – Family Dollar

4. D – Jennifer Aniston

5. C – Dairy Queen

6. B – Nike

7. A – True

8. D – The Hunger Games

9. C – Charlotte Hornets

10. B – Charlotte Sting

11. B – Spectrum Center

12. A – True

13. D – Charlotte FC

14. D – Charlotte does not have an MLB team.

15. C – Imaginon

16. A – True

17. B – NASCAR

18. A – CLT

19. D – Pimento

20. A – True

DID YOU KNOW?

1. The 1994 NCAA Final Four was held at the Charlotte Coliseum.

2. According to payscale.com, the cost of living in Charlotte is 5% lower than the national average.

3. There are over 3,000 international refugees from over 40 different countries living in Charlotte today.

4. For over 50 years, Charlotte led the nation in gold production until the California Gold Rush of 1848.

5. Astronaut Charlie Duke was born in Charlotte on October 3, 1935. At age 36, he became the 10th man to walk on the moon.

6. Charles Sifford was born in Charlotte in 1922. He was the first African-American to participate in the PGA Tour, which got him the nickname, "The Jackie Robinson of Golf."

7. Harvey Gantt was the first African-American student admitted to Clemson University and later became the first African-American mayor of Charlotte.

8. During the Civil War, Charlotte was the site of a Confederate headquarters and hospital.

9. The Carolinas Aviation Museum is an aviation museum is located at the Charlotte Douglas International Airport. Its

main attraction is the Airbus A320 used on US Airways Flight 1549 (The Miracle on the Hudson River).

10. Charlotte residents are referred to as "Charlotteans."

CHAPTER 17:

FIELD MOUSE

QUIZ TIME!

1. Where was Sam Mills born?

    a. Charlotte, North Carolina

    b. Oakland, California

    c. Neptune City, New Jersey

    d. Detroit, Michigan

2. Sam Mills played his entire NFL career with the Carolina Panthers.

    a. True

    b. False

3. Where did Sam Mills attend college?

    a. The University of Alabama

    b. University of South Carolina

    c. San Diego State University

    d. Montclair State University

4. What coaching role did Sam Mills hold with the Carolina Panthers from 1998 through 2004?

a. Head coach

b. Defensive assistant

c. Linebackers coach

d. Both B and C

5. After being diagnosed with terminal intestinal cancer, Sam Mills urged the Panthers team to "_____" in an emotional pregame speech. This phrase has become a slogan for the team ever since.

a. Keep going

b. Keep fighting

c. Keep pounding

d. Keep pushing

6. Sam Mills's son, Sam Mills III, is currently the defensive line coach for which NFL team?

a. San Francisco 49ers

b. Washington Football Team

c. New Orleans Saints

d. Indianapolis Colts

7. Sam Mills's number 51 was retired by the Carolina Panthers at the start of the 2005 NFL season, making it the first number the Panthers retired.

a. True

b. False

8. How many Pro Bowls was Sam Mills named to during his 12-season NFL career?

a. 2

b. 3

c. 5

d. 7

9. How many times was Sam Mills named a First Team All-Pro?

   a. 0

   b. 1

   c. 2

   d. 3

10. Before the start of every home game, the Panthers have an honorary drummer bang a "Keep Pounding" drum. Which NBA star was the drummer before Super Bowl 50?

   a. LeBron James

   b. Kobe Bryant

   c. Steph Curry

   d. Kawhi Leonard

11. Sam Mills also played in the USFL. Which team did he play for from 1983 through 1985?

   a. New Jersey Generals

   b. Denver Gold

   c. Arizona Outlaws

   d. Philadelphia/Baltimore Stars

12. Sam Mills was the only Panthers player to start every game during the Panthers' first three seasons.

   a. True

   b. False

13. In high school, Sam Mills played both football and
_____.

    a. Baseball
    b. Wrestling
    c. Soccer
    d. Golf

14. Sam Mills signed with the Cleveland Browns as an undrafted free agent in 1981 but was released after the conclusion of the preseason.

    a. True
    b. False

15. In 1982, Sam Mills signed with the _____ of the Canadian Football League but was released before the season began.

    a. Calgary Stampeders
    b. Ottawa Redblacks
    c. Toronto Argonauts
    d. Winnipeg Blue Bombers

16. Sam Mills's speed, which was surprising for a man of his size, earned him the nickname "Field Mouse."

    a. True
    b. False

17. Sam Mills was elected to the Louisiana Sports Hall of Fame in _____.

    a. 1998
    b. 1999

c. 2000

d. 2001

18. Sam Mills was elected to the Sports Hall of Fame of New Jersey in _____.

    a. 2001

    b. 2003

    c. 2004

    d. 2005

19. Sam Mills was inducted into the College Football Hall of Fame in _____.

    a. 2005

    b. 2007

    c. 2009

    d. 2012

20. During his time in the NFL, Sam Mills started 173 of 181 games.

    a. True

    b. False

QUIZ ANSWERS

1. C – Neptune City, New Jersey
2. B – False (He played with the Panthers and New Orleans Saints.)
3. D – Montclair State University
4. D – Both B and C
5. C – Keep pounding
6. B – Washington Football Team
7. A – True
8. C – 5
9. B – 1
10. C – Steph Curry
11. D – Philadelphia/Baltimore Stars
12. A – True
13. B – Wrestling
14. A – True
15. C – Toronto Argonauts
16. A – True
17. D – 2001
18. B – 2003
19. C – 2009
20. A – True

DID YOU KNOW?

1. Sam Mills is a member of both the Carolina Panthers' Hall of Honor and the New Orleans Saints' Hall of Fame. His number 51 is the only number retired by the Carolina Panthers.

2. Sam Mills's fifth Pro Bowl appearance in 1996 at the age of 37 made him the oldest defender to be invited to a Pro Bowl at the time.

3. After battling cancer for nearly two years, Sam Mills died at his home in Charlotte on the morning of April 18, 2005.

4. Although he never won a Super Bowl championship, Sam Mills did win two championships with the Philadelphia Stars in the USFL.

5. Sam Mills was never drafted into the NFL. After the Stars won the 1985 USFL title, their head coach Jim Mora was signed to coach the New Orleans Saints, and Mills followed him. Mora called Mills: "The best player I ever coached."

6. Sam Mills was a member of the "Dome Patrol," the legendary linebacking corps that led the Saints defense in the 1990s. Other members of the "Dome Patrol" were Rickey Jackson, Vaughan Johnson, and Pat Swilling. All four "Dome Patrol" members were on the Saints roster for seven seasons, from 1986 to 1992, and the players combined for 18 Pro Bowls while with the team together. All four

linebackers were invited to the Pro Bowl in 1992, which was the only time four linebackers from one team made a Pro Bowl together.

7. Sam Mills recorded 1,319 tackles, 20.5 sacks, 11 interceptions, and four touchdowns during his 12 seasons in the NFL.

8. In August 2003, when Sam Mills was diagnosed with intestinal cancer, he was told he had only a few months to live. He underwent chemotherapy and radiation, yet continued to coach the Panthers.

9. For the 2012 NFL season, Nike had "Keep Pounding" sewn on the inside collars of Panthers jerseys in honor of Mills.

10. Long Branch High School honors Sam Mills to this day by hanging his high school jersey and his NFL jersey in the school's gym.

CHAPTER 18:

SUPER CAM

QUIZ TIME!

1. Where was Cam Newton born?

    a. San Diego, California

    b. Atlanta, Georgia

    c. Charleston, South Carolina

    d. Boston, Massachusetts

2. As of the end of the 2020 NFL season, Cam Newton has played for the Carolina Panthers and the New England Patriots.

    a. True

    b. False

3. Cam Newton was named the NFL MVP in _____.

    a. 2012

    b. 2013

    c. 2014

    d. 2015

4. Where did Cam Newton attend college?

    a. University of Michigan
    b. Penn State University
    c. Auburn University
    d. University of Tennessee

5. How many Pro Bowls has Cam Newton been named to (as of the end of the 2020 season)?

    a. 0
    b. 1
    c. 2
    d. 3

6. Cam Newton was named the Pepsi NFL Rookie of the Year in _____.

    a. 2010
    b. 2011
    c. 2012
    d. 2013

7. Cam Newton currently holds the NFL record for most rushing touchdowns by a quarterback.

    a. True
    b. False

8. How many times has Cam Newton been named a First Team All-Pro (as of the end of the 2019 season)?

    a. 0
    b. 1
    c. 2
    d. 3

9. In 2015, Cam Newton graduated from Auburn University with a degree in _____.

   a. Journalism

   b. Psychology

   c. Business

   d. Sociology

10. Cam Newton holds the NFL record for most combined touchdowns for a rookie in NFL history, with _____.

   a. 25

   b. 30

   c. 35

   d. 40

11. In 2013, Cam Newton partnered with Belk on his own clothing line called "_____ by Cam Newton."

   a. WIN

   b. MADE

   c. CREATE

   d. LIVE

12. Cam Newton won the Heisman Trophy in 2010.

   a. True

   b. False

13. Cam Newton was the first rookie quarterback in NFL history to throw for _____ yards in his NFL debut.

   a. 200

   b. 300

   c. 400

   d. 500

14. With the ____ pick in the 1st round of the 2011 NFL Draft, the Carolina Panthers selected Cam Newton.

    a. 1st

    b. 2nd

    c. 3rd

    d. 4th

15. Cam Newton was named the NFL Offensive Player of the Year in _____.

    a. 2013

    b. 2015

    c. 2017

    d. 2018

16. Both Cam Newton's father and Cam Newton's older brother played in the NFL as well.

    a. True

    b. False

17. How many times was Cam Newton named the NFC Offensive Player of the Week with the Carolina Panthers?

    a. 5

    b. 8

    c. 10

    d. 12

18. As of March 2019, Cam Newton is a vegan.

    a. True

    b. False

19. How many Super Bowl championships has Cam Newton won (as of the end of the 2019 season)?

    a. 0

    b. 1

    c. 2

    d. 3

20. Cam Newton holds the Panthers franchise record for most NFC Offensive Player of the Week Awards in a single season, with five.

    a. True

    b. False

QUIZ ANSWERS

1. B – Atlanta, Georgia

2. A – True

3. D – 2015

4. C – Auburn University

5. D – 3

6. B – 2011

7. A – True

8. B – 1

9. D – Sociology

10. C – 35

11. B – MADE

12. A – True

13. C – 400

14. A – 1st

15. B – 2015

16. A – True

17. C – 10

18. A – True

19. A – 0

20. A – True

DID YOU KNOW?

1. Cam Newton was the second African-American quarterback to win the NFL MVP Award and the first to solely receive it.

2. On December 9, 2014, Cam Newton was involved in a car crash in Charlotte . His vehicle flipped and he suffered two back fractures.

3. Cam Newton has seven children: Jaden, Shakira, Chosen, Sovereign-Dior, Camidas, Caesar, and Cashmere.

4. Cam Newton owns a restaurant/cigar bar called Fellaship near Mercedes-Benz Stadium in Atlanta, Georgia.

5. In addition to playing football, Cam Newton is a motivational speaker.

6. When Cam Newton became the New England Patriots' quarterback in 2020, he became the first starting quarterback for the Patriots other than Tom Brady in 18 years.

7. Cam Newton had college football stints at Florida and Blinn before deciding to play at Auburn University.

8. Cam Newton goes by the nickname "Super Cam" or "Superman" due to his touchdown celebration.

9. During a press conference in 2017, Cam Newton was asked a question by Jourdan Rodrigue, a female sportswriter,

regarding passing routes. Newton smirked and said, "It's funny to hear a female talk about routes." This was considered sexist and highly controversial.

10. After missing the majority of the 2019 season due to surgery, Cam Newton was released by the Carolina Panthers. He then became the quarterback of the New England Patriots in 2020, where he struggled.

CONCLUSION

Learn anything new? Now you truly are the ultimate Panthers fan! Not only did you learn about the Panthers of the modern era, but you also expanded your knowledge back to the early days of the franchise.

You learned about the Panthers' origins and history. You learned about the history of their uniforms and jersey numbers. You identified some famous quotes, and you read some of the craziest nicknames of all time. You learned more about former star quarterback, Cam Newton. You also learned about the amazing Julius Peppers and the late Sam Mills. You were amazed by Panthers stats and recalled some of the team's most infamous trades and draft picks of all time. You broke down your knowledge by offense, defense, and special teams. You looked back on the Panthers' Super Bowl appearances, playoff feats, and the awards that came before, after, and during them. You also learned about the Panthers' fiercest rivalries, both inside and outside of their division.

Every team in the NFL has a storied history, but the Panthers have one of the most memorable of all. They have fought year after year since their establishment in 1995 with the backing of their devoted fans. Being the ultimate Panthers fan takes knowledge and a whole lot of patience, which you tested with this book. Whether you knew every answer or were stumped by several questions, you learned some of the most interesting history that the game of football has to offer.

The deep history of the Panthers represents what we all love about the game of football. The heart, the determination, the tough times, and the unexpected moments, plus the players that inspire us and encourage us to do our best because, even if you get knocked down, there is always another game and another (Sun)day.

With players like Teddy Bridgewater, Christian McCaffrey, and Joey Slye, the future for the Panthers continues to look bright. They have a lot to prove but there is no doubt that this franchise will continue to be one of the most competitive teams in the NFL each season.

It's a new decade, which means there is a clean slate, ready to continue writing the history of the Carolina Panthers. The ultimate Panthers fan cannot wait to see what's to come for their beloved team. Keep Pounding!

Made in the USA
Monee, IL
06 July 2022

99204425R00085